CW00349108

* The very first drawing of Jeff by Allan aged 22, 1993

# THE VERY BEST OF THE ODD SQUAD

ALLAN PLENDERLEITH

RAVETTE PUBLISHING

For more books + apps by Allan visit
www.allanplenderleith.com

First published 2013 by
Ravette Publishing Limited
PO Box 876, Horsham, West Sussex RH12 9GH



ISBN: 978-1-84161-376-5

Vicious traps, poison, mouldy cheese –
clearly, this madman had to be stopped

For Mum, thanks for laughing

x

The banana Jeff bought last week
had turned bad

Jeff makes a cat flap

It wasn't so much the poo in his slipper that bothered Jeff – more the smirk on his dog's face

One dark evening, Jeff became a sad victim of the phantom head and bum swapper

Never sneeze while squeezing toothpaste

Jeff enters a
'go for another wipe or leave it'
dilemma

After repeated banging and a loud 'crack',
Jeff's door finally closed

Jeff had an annoying
hare in his mouth

Far from saggy boobs being a burden, they can become handy holders for cigarettes and pencils!

Although the survivors had no food and were miles from anywhere - they needn't worry- because Jeff had remembered the flares

Billy's rabbit becomes the ill-fated star of a You've Been Framed clip

Billy's biology lesson turns to the importance of jobby types

Someone had sharpened the strings on Jeff's guitar

While on his way to the shops,
Billy gets stung by a bee

Billy and Moira carry out a hardness test on Cyril

Never blow-off wearing a g-string

For her birthday, Maude's boyfriend gives her multiple organisms

Never underestimate a hamster

Jeff plays that popular party game, 'Guess the Real Walnut Whirl'

Maude looks up an old friend

Billy is about to stamp when he feels a light tap on his shoulder

The morning after, Jeff's mouth felt like he'd licked a badger's arse.

When Jeff got back to his car there was a big bird dropping on it.

Maude's friend was a big slapper.

Maude had actually asked Jeff to put some Barry White on the stereo.

Jeff's bogie flick went in the wrong direction.

Never burp whilst kissing.

After seeing his friend's method of milk frothing, Jeff decides not to have a cappuccino after all.

Unfortunately in the confusion and terror of being chased by a dog, Ginger had mistaken the air vent for the cat flap.

Clearly, the cat had finally figured out how to work eBay.

When he eats in a pub, Jeff always orders chicken in a basque.

Freddy the hamster prefers cookies with chocolate chips.

Judging by all the 'chocolate kisses'
on the floor, the dog's bum
was in need of a wash again.

It was so cold Alf could see Lily's nipples.

The best thing about flying was the complimentary nuts.

As Alf got older, he got into crosswords.

Jeff receives a large Czech
through the post.

Billy spends the day in 'da hood'.

The morning after beers and kebabs,
Jeff woke up with a disguising
film on his teeth.

Jeff had a feeling the dog
had worms again.

Dug was pleasantly surprised when, during their passionate embrace, Barbara began tickling his bum.

Once again,
Jeff's cartoonist was drunk.

Although they'd lost both wings
Dug brought down the plane safely
thanks to his 70's style lapels.

Billy had invented a fun new game –
spot the elderly squirrel!

Jeff's flies were down.

Wow! Jeff had left a vegetable curry out for him – AND it was warm!

Well, the unusual flower certainly
looked pretty
but it smelled terrible!

Dug suddenly discovers the Indian meal came with a free nan.

A man on the underground gave
Jeff the willies.

Once again, Billy's goldfish
had diarrhoea.

Billy finally finds out what happened
to his good crayons.

Jeff had learned an important lesson:
never leave a depressed hamster alone
with fresh spaghetti.

Jeff liked to hang out with his mates
down the pub.

During his long journey, Jeff stops off in the hard shoulder for a sneaky wee.

Once again, Jeff's dog had swallowed the icing bag nozzle.

Maude was really pleased with her new jogging bottoms.

As he got older,
Alf began having joint trouble.

It was only when blowing up his new sex doll that Jeff realised he'd been given the wrong model.

As a louder and more satisfying alternative to clapping, Lily slaps together the loose skin under her arms.

At the pub, Dug and his mates always put their money in a kitty.

The world's first attempt at mouth-to-mouth resuscitation on a dog was not a complete success.

Jeff loved potato wedgies.

Billy impresses the girls with his very own "poo bear".

Having run out of condoms,
Jeff quickly improvises.

Once again, Jeff was overdrawn.

Jeff was really into onion rings.

At the barbers, Jeff asked for a Number 2.

Jeff knew the dog was healthy
because he had a lovely wet nose.

Jeff suspected the doner kebab wasn't entirely made from lamb.

Suddenly, as the light shone through her dress, Dug realised his date wasn't always called Brenda.

It was only after their enthusiastic rumpy that Jeff and Maude realised the dog was in fact under the bed.

Jeff treats Maude to a slap-up meal.

Once again, Jeff had to work late because they were short-staffed.

Maude had locked her shelf out again.

Somehow, during the night, the dog
had mastered the pencil sharpener.

Suddenly during her sexy dance, Maude's suspenders snapped.

Why older ladies should avoid going on roundabouts.

The hamster's trapped wind problem was back.

Jeff visits the doctor to have
a worrying mole removed.

Men were still turned off by Maude's armpit hair, despite arranging them in attractive plaits.

Just at the point of climax,
Dug withdrew.

Billy decides to switch Wilbur the worm
to a high fibre diet.

Dug had actually asked for
an Apple Mac.

At a critical point in the third set,
Alf realised the ball was out.

Once again, the sat-nav was surprisingly accurate.

Dug hates it when he gets a sweater on his birthday.

Jeff had ordered the bitter shandy.

Not fair!
We wanna play!!

Billy got a new computer console
but the batteries were not included.

Jeff took his car in for a service.

Unfortunately, the cat had ignored
Maude's warnings to stop licking itself
so much.

At the Indian, Jeff regretted ordering the "Chicken Sag".

Jeff did a good job of
child-proofing the house.

As the fire was dying down,
Alf asks Lily to
chuck on some more coal.

How to tell you are in the middle of
a credit crunch.

Maude had mistakenly bought extra thick cream.

Jeff had asked the optician if he could have his eyes checked.

Once again, Jeff was filling up
at the petrol station.

Whilst cooking a Thai meal,
Jeff adds garlic, chilli and some ginger.

Before laying the patio slabs,
Jeff put down some hard core.

Dug accidentally pressed the hash key on his computer again.

As Jeff entered the remote rural pub, he had a feeling the locals were all in-bread.

Jeff had bought an iPod Touchy.

Jeff had actually asked the waiter to make his curry "a little hotter".

Jeff had a strange feeling Maude
was wearing no underwear again.

For his birthday, Jeff got a "paintball" voucher.

Once again, Maude had bought the wrong panty liner.

Billy had asked for a Playstation
for his birthday.

To save money, Jeff rides on
pubic transport.

Whilst installing a new computer programme, Jeff had a problem with the set-up wizard.

Jeff makes sure he regularly tests the smoke alarm.

As Brenda bent over to tee up,
Jeff whacked one out in the rough.

The morning after her birthday, Maude experienced headaches, fatigue and nausea.

By simply using some rubber bands,
Lily instantly had younger, smoother skin.

For some reason, Lily found the porridge difficult to stir that morning.

As Maude got undressed, she shook off the feeling she was being watched – safe in the knowledge she was 20 storeys high.

DOG
AP

Having lost the wine stopper,
Maude improvises.

Maude no longer needed a can opener,
not since Buck-toothed Bobby
moved in next door.

The "make an animal out of food" project had backfired.

To achieve a younger, perkier look,
Lily employs the services of
Bobo and Chico, the bald circus dwarves.

Suddenly the wise men regretted buying the cheap sat-nav.

Every year Santa dreads delivering presents to the Single Women's Foundation.

What happens when the Christmas tree fairy goes to the loo.

Although he couldn't talk, Rudolf had learned to communicate in other ways.

# Other books by Allan Plenderleith: